I love you Mummy

igloobooks

igloobooks

Published in 2017
by Igloo Books Ltd
Cottage Farm
Sywell
NN6 0BJ
www.igloobooks.com

REX001 1216
2 4 6 8 10 9 7 5 3 1
ISBN 978-1-78557-474-0

Produced under license for

carte blanche

© 2016 Carte Blanche Greetings Limited ® cbg.co.uk
The Tiny Tatty Teddy Logo and the Me to You
oval are registered Trade Marks of Carte Blanche
Greetings Limited.

Designed by Elitsa Veshkova
Written by Claire Mowat

Printed and manufactured in China

This igloo book belongs to:

....

Mummy, I love you more than the world's biggest hug.

Cuddles with you make me feel warm and snug.

I love our fun games when my toys get in a muddle.

You chase me...

... and tickle me...

... then give me a cuddle.

I love the days when we go out and explore.

We find lots of treasure, then we find even more!

I love it when music makes us dance, sing and wriggle.

Our moves are so silly and we start to giggle!

The story I like most is always the same.

I love it when you read it again and again.

Mummy, I love you and when I have money to spare,

I'll buy you lots of things to show you I care.

I love it when we look at the sparkly stars at night.

I want to give one to you that's shiny and bright.

It's such fun when we learn new things together.

2+2

I want to be just like you. You're super clever.

At bedtime, after my bath...

.. when I'm all nice and clean.

You sing me a lullaby and I start to dream.

I've been trying to tell you, but I'm sure you already knew.

You are the best mummy ever and I love you!

I LOVE YOU MUMMY!